Study Guide for Readings in Contemporary Sexuality

Second Edition

Albert J. Angelo, M.S. Ed.
Ivy Chen, MPH
John P. Elia, Ph.D.
San Francisco State University

KENDALL/HUNT PUBLISHING COMPANY
4050 Westmark Drive   Dubuque, Iowa 52002

C O N T E N T S

P R E F A C E

This study guide is intended to assist you while reading Readings in Contemporary Sexuality. The chapters in this study guide correspond to the chapters in the main text. Each chapter in this study guide is concise. We believe that we have captured the "essential ingredients" in each of the following chapters by developing exercises that will not only help you master important concepts from the text but also will likely facilitate personal insights about contemporary sexuality. Our aim was to write a study guide that would "speak" to the relevance of students' lives, and not simply amount to another document filled with highly abstract material to be learned by rote memorization. It is our hope that you will find this study guide interesting, thought-provoking, and relevant to your life.

Each chapter contains the same series of exercises. Each chapter begins with a 75- to 150-word summary of the corresponding chapter in the main text. These summaries are included to summarize the main points and the general thrust of the chapter. Following the summary, several identification items are listed. In this section we have listed important names, concepts, and terms. To get the most out of this exercise, students should locate each identification item in the chapter and write a few sentences or a small paragraph about it. For each item, write a definition followed by how this particular item is significant to the chapter in which it appears and to contemporary sexuality in general. The next section of each chapter of the study guide contains sample test items. In this section you will find five true-and-false items and five multiple-choice questions. Each item covers a different aspect of the chapter. In other words, when you have finished both practice tests—true-and-false and multiple-choice items—you will have covered all of the major aspects of the chapter. The next section contains a few discussion items. Please review the chapter and write down some points you would like to raise in a discussion about the discussion item(s). Next, you will find a few study questions, which are designed to prepare you for essay tests and class discussions. Following this section, you will find the answers to the true-and-false and multiple-choice items.

When you have finished all of the sections of each chapter, you can be assured that you will be very well acquainted with the chapter. Again, not only will you have a thorough understanding of the contents of the chapter but also you will likely gain much personal insight from the process of working your way through the material.

Albert J. Angelo, MS.Ed
Ivy Chen, MPH
John P. Elia, Ph.D.
San Francisco, California

SECTION I

Sexuality in History,
Culture, and the Media

CHAPTER 1

The History and Future of Sex

Marty Klein

SUMMARY

This article discusses how society developments, including technological advances and social changes, have had great impact on sexuality, whether it be directly or indirectly. Invention of the birth control pill, vasectomy and other reproductive discoveries had a very direct influence on sexuality and relationships. Events such as war, invention of the VCR, and even the installation of gaslights in theaters had an indirect effect on gender roles, sex and relationships.

IDENTIFICATIONS: NAMES/CONCEPTS/TERMS

- Baird v. Eisenstadt
- Roe v. Wade
- Hysteria
- "Self-abuse"
- Demographic trends
- Technologic trends
- Cultural trends

SAMPLE TEST ITEMS: TRUE/FALSE

1. T   F   The VCR's popularity was due to the wide availability of low-cost porn videotapes that people can now watch in the privacy of their own homes.

2. T   F   The author alleges that an industry involving the increasing population of the elderly and their sexual issues will experience a boon as adults' life spans increase.

3. T   F   Though the telephone had an impact on past generations' sexual relationships, it seems to have less importance in today's teens' relationships.

4. T   F   The author claims that the line between contraception and abortion is disappearing.

MULTIPLE CHOICE

1. "Dating" as an adolescent institution became popularized because of:
   a. the Vietnam War.
   b. the invention of the birth control pill.
   c. WWII.
   d. the Depression.
   e. prohibition.

2. The court case Baird v. Eisenstadt legalized:
   a. Abortion.
   b. The right for people to use birth control even if they were single.
   c. Interracial marriage.
   d. Same-sex marriage.
   e. Prostitution.

3. The author claims that a huge demographic change is that after school, kids are now:
   a. involved in after-school sports programs.
   b. enrolled in tutoring programs.
   c. unsupervised at home, possibly leading to behaviors such as smoking and having sex.
   d. spending time with their moms and grandmothers.
   e. working part-time jobs.

DISCUSSION ITEMS

How is sex and relationships different now than in your parents' generation?

Of the differences you have listed in the previous questions, what do you think were the biggest societal influences that caused these changes?

STUDY QUESTIONS

What are some of the social and sexual impacts of having college student groups that are much more varied in age and culture?

Explain what the author means by claiming that infidelity is getting more difficult to define.

ANSWERS

True/False:
  1. T
  2. T
  3. F
  4. T

Multiple Choice:

  1. D
  2. B
  3. C

CHAPTER 2

Why Do We Know So Little about Human Sex?

Anne Fausto-Sterling, Ph.D.

SUMMARY

In this chapter, the author addresses the issue of why we as individuals and as a society know so little about human sexuality. Sexology, the study of human sexual behavior, only began in the twentieth century and is continually challenged by conservative political and social forces. We know so little, the author argues, because certain influential people and powerful organizations are working to keep it that way.

IDENTIFICATIONS: NAMES/CONCEPTS/TERMS

- Alfred Kinsey
- Institute for the Study of Sexual Behavior
- Jesse Helms
- "Homosexualities"
- Magnus Hirschfeld
- Sexology
- Simon LeVay

SAMPLE TEST ITEMS: TRUE/FALSE

1. T   F   The author believes the US government strongly supports sex research.

2. T   F   "Homosexualities" is another term for bisexuality.

3. T   F   Alfred Kinsey did not believe people could be bisexual.

4. T   F   Simon LeVay studied the physiological differences in the brains of heterosexual and homosexual males.

5. T   F   Jesse Helms does not support gay rights or research examining homosexual behavior.

MULTIPLE CHOICE

1. In 1991, this person founded the Institute for the Study of Sexual Behavior in Germany:
   a. Alfred Kinsey
   b. Jesse Helms
   c. Magnus Hirschfeld
   d. Simon LeVay
   e. Havelock Ellis

2. This person conducted the first and most famous modern scientific sex survey:
   a. Alfred Kinsey
   b. Havelock Ellis
   c. Richard von Krafft-Ebing
   d. Magnus Hirschfeld
   e. Simon LeVay

3. This person is against federal funding for sexuality studies:
   a. Michael Lee
   b. Howard Jackson
   c. Alfred Kinsey
   d. Magnus Hirschfeld
   e. Jesse Helms

4. The term "homosexualities" refers to:
   a. two gay men in a monogamous relationship
   b. the diversity of homosexual behaviors
   c. the diversity of heterosexual behaviors
   d. two gay men in a nonmonogamous relationship
   e. two lesbian women in a monogamous relationship

5. Simon LeVay's research on sexual orientation has been criticized because he assumed all his subjects were:
   a. heterosexual men
   b. homosexual men
   c. bisexual men
   d. heterosexual women
   e. not bisexual men

DISCUSSION ITEMS

Do you feel the federal government should financially support sex research? Explain.

Do you feel your college should support human sexuality research? Explain.

STUDY QUESTIONS

Why does the author feel sex research is important? How can sex research benefit society?

Why is it difficult to study human sexuality? What are the challenges to this type of research?

ANSWERS

True/False:
1. F
2. F
3. F
4. T
5. T

Multiple Choice:
1. C
2. A
3. E
4. B
5. E

CHAPTER 3

Influences of Culture on Asian Americans' Sexuality

Sumie Okazaki

SUMMARY

Culture plays an important role in shaping one's values, attitudes, and beliefs. This article examines how culture influences the views and sexual behaviors of Asian American men and women. The research suggests Asian American adolescents and young adults are more sexually conservative in their attitudes and actions while adult Asian Americans may not receive appropriate medical care such as routine mammogram screenings or reproductive health care services. Interestingly, as Asian Americans become acculturated into American society, they adopt more consistent views with the White American norm.

IDENTIFICATIONS: NAMES/CONCEPTS/TERMS

- Culture
- Acculturation

SAMPLE TEST ITEMS: TRUE/FALSE

1. T   F   Relative to other US ethnic groups, Asian American adolescents and young adults show more sexually conservative attitudes and behaviors but engage in intimate sexual intercourse at an earlier age.

2. T   F   Asian American women appear more reluctant to obtain sexual and reproductive health care services.

3. T   F   Research suggests the prevalence rate of sexual abuse in Asian American communities may be lower than those of other groups.

4. T   F   The term "Asian American" refers to someone whose family was originally from China or Japan but not from North or South Korea.

5. T   F   Expressions of sexual activity outside of marriage are considered highly inappropriate in most Asian cultures.

MULTIPLE CHOICE

1. Research cited in this article states Asian American adolescents in homes where English is the primary language spoken were more likely than other Asian Americans to have:
   a. Engaged in homosexual activity
   b. Practiced intercourse with birth control
   c. Engaged in heterosexual genital sexual activities
   d. Increased STD infections including Chlamydia and gonorrhea
   e. Increased pregnancy rates

2. Research suggests Asian American women are:
   a. More sexually active than African American women
   b. Less likely than White American women to get mammograms
   c. Less likely than Hispanic women to use condoms
   d. More likely than White American women to engage in homosexual behavior
   e. Less likely than African American women to use condoms

3. Research suggests more than half of gay and lesbian Asian American men and women:
   a. Are infected with HIV
   b. Are more comfortable in a queer community than an Asian American community
   c. Are less comfortable in a queer community than an Asian American community
   d. Are forced to leave home when their parents discover their sexual orientation
   e. Do not practice safer sex using condoms or latex barrier methods

4. According to the article, the level of sexual aggression in Asian American communities is reported to be:
   a. Lower than other ethnic communities
   b. Higher than other ethnic communities
   c. Similarly equal to other ethnic communities
   d. Higher than White American communities
   e. Equal to White American communities

5. According to the article, research suggests college age Asian American men and women are more likely to:
   a. Be virgins as compared to White American college students
   b. Be non-virgins as compared to White American college students
   c. Contract more STDs than Hispanic college students
   d. Contract more STDs than African American college students
   e. Engage in unprotected sex as compared to Hispanic American college students

DISCUSSION ITEMS

How does your cultural background influence your values, beliefs, and behaviors as they relate to human sexuality issues?

How does the predominant American culture, including movies, music, and advertising influence your values, beliefs, and behaviors as they relate to human sexuality issues?

STUDY QUESTIONS

How does culture influence the attitudes, values, and behaviors of Asian American young men and women?

How does acculturation influence the attitudes, values, and behaviors of Asian American men and women?

ANSWERS

True/False:
1. F
2. T
3. T
4. F
5. T

Multiple Choice:
1. C
2. B
3. B
4. A
5. A

C H A P T E R **4**

Mass Media Influences on Sexuality

Jane D. Brown

SUMMARY

This article examines how the mass media may influence one's attitudes, perceptions, and behaviors as related to issues in human sexuality. The author examines the mass media's impact using three distinct theoretical perspectives and encourages further research on this important and contemporary topic.

IDENTIFICATIONS: NAMES/CONCEPTS/TERMS

- Agenda Setting/Framing
- Cultivation
- Cognitive Social Learning Theory

SAMPLE TEST ITEMS: TRUE/FALSE

1. T F Gay, lesbian, bisexual, and transgender youth rarely find themselves represented in the mainstream media.

2. T F Almost 50% of programs on television that include sexual content mention the need to use contraceptives or protection against sexually transmitted diseases.

3. T   F   No studies show a relationship between viewing sexually explicit content on television and increased sexual behavior among adolescent males and females.

4. T   F   African Americans typically view less television than Whites.

5. T   F   Agenda Setting/Framing theory states that people will imitate behaviors of others when they see those people being rewarded for their behavior.

MULTIPLE CHOICE

1. In 2001, this word was the most popular search term on the internet:
   a. Intercourse
   b. Orgasm
   c. Virginity
   d. Vagina
   e. Sex

2. What are the three "C's" of responsible sexual behavior?
   a. Commitment, contraceptives, and consideration of consequences
   b. Commitment, climax, and communication
   c. Communication, contraceptives, and containment
   d. Contraceptives, communication, and consent
   e. Consent, communication, and consideration of consequences

3. Which of the following was a theoretical perspective used to examine the media's influence on one's sexual attitudes and behavior?
   a. Agenda Setting/Framing
   b. Behavioral Reinforcement Analysis
   c. Freudian Analysis
   d. Exposure Effect
   e. Hawthorne Effect

4. According to this theory, television programs act as powerful storytellers in American society.
   a. Fictional saturation theory
   b. Ascribed viewer saturation theory
   c. Cultivation theory
   d. Social order theory
   e. Media saturation theory

5. Studies conclude the media:
   a. Frequently talk about homosexuality issues
   b. Rarely show sexually responsible models of sexual behavior on TV
   c. Often talk about condom use when issues of homosexuality arise
   d. Frequently talk about abortion issues during daytime soap operas
   e. Rarely show sexually explicit content in non prime-time hours

DISCUSSION ITEMS

How do you feel the mass media, including television programming, influence one's values and viewpoints as they relate to human sexuality issues?

Do you feel mass media images of sexual behavior encourage young men and women to become sexually active? Explain your position.

STUDY QUESTIONS

How does Cognitive Social Learning Theory and Cultivation Theory explain how young men and women are influenced by sexual content viewed on television?

How was early coverage of the AIDS epidemic depicted by the media? What later shifted the media's view of HIV infection from one of morality to one of a public health threat?

ANSWERS

True/False:
1. T
2. F
3. F
4. F
5. F

Multiple Choice:
1. E
2. A
3. A
4. C
5. B

SECTION II

Adolescence and Sexuality

C H A P T E R 5

Early Sexual Maturation Increasingly Common among Girls

Henry J. Kaiser Family Foundation

SUMMARY

Young girls are hitting puberty at much younger ages than their moms. There also seems to be a racial difference, with more black girls developing at an earlier rate than white girls. Even at age 7, more than a quarter of young black girls have already shown early signs of puberty as compared to 7% of white girls. Several theories of why girls are developing early are presented in the article.

IDENTIFICATIONS: NAMES/CONCEPTS/TERMS

- Precocious puberty
- Breast buds
- Lupron
- Phthalates

SAMPLE TEST ITEMS: TRUE/FALSE

1. T   F   By age 8, nearly 50% of black girls and 15% of white girls begin to develop breasts or pubic hair.

2. T   F   By age 9, both black and white girls have the same rate of puberty development.

MULTIPLE CHOICE

1. The average age of first menstruation is about:
   a. 9
   b. 11
   c. 12
   d. 14
   e. 17

2. The leading theory as to what is causing the shift in earlier physical developments in girls is:
   a. exposure to environmental estrogens.
   b. increase in girls' body fat and childhood obesity.
   c. increased exposure to artificial lighting.
   d. exposure to chemicals in plastics called phthalates.
   e. better nutrition.

DISCUSSION ITEMS

Why do you think boys are not yet experiencing a similar jumpstart to puberty?

STUDY QUESTION

Why are parents worried about their daughters exhibiting early signs of sexual development?

ANSWERS

True/False:
 1. T
 2. F

Multiple Choice:
 1. C
 2. B

CHAPTER 6

Decline in Teen Pregnancy Due to Both Less Sexual Activity and More Contraceptive Use: More Evidence That Young People Benefit from a Comprehensive Approach to Sexuality

SIECUS

SUMMARY

In the ten years between the early 90s and the early 2000s, teen pregnancy has dropped 33%. Much of the credit is due to comprehensive sexuality health education, which discusses abstinence as well as contraception and sexually transmitted diseases. Comprehensive sex ed promotes responsible decision making, which in turn influences teens to delay sexual intercourse and to use contraceptives correctly if they choose to become sexually active.

IDENTIFICATIONS: NAMES/CONCEPTS/TERMS

- Sexuality Information and Education Council of the United States (SIECUS)
- Comprehensive sexuality health education
- Abstinence-only-until-marriage programs

SAMPLE TEST ITEMS: TRUE/FALSE

1. T   F   According to the spokesperson for SIECUS, more young people are choosing to delay sexual intercourse.

2. T   F   Though the article claims that teens are using more contraceptives, they are actually relying on ineffective methods such as withdrawal.

3. T   F   Between the late 1990s and the mid-2000s, federal and state lawmakers have spent a huge amount of money on comprehensive sexuality health education.

MULTIPLE CHOICE

1. A type of sex education that SIECUS does not support is:
   a. teaching of birth control.
   b. teaching of condoms and safer sex.
   c. comprehensive sex ed.
   d. abstinence-only sex ed.
   e. teaching of relationships.

2. According to the article, the percentage of young people who are sexually active before high school graduation is around:
   a. 20%
   b. 40%
   c. 60%
   d. 80%
   e. 100%

DISCUSSION ITEM

What do you think it takes to lower teen pregnancy rates?

STUDY QUESTION

What are the statistics on condom use by teens?

ANSWERS

True/False:
 1. T
 2. F
 3. F

Multiple Choice:
 1. D
 2. C

C H A P T E R

Relationship Type, Goals Predict the Consistency of Teenagers' Condom Use

Alan Guttmacher Institute

SUMMARY

Adolescents who use condoms consistently differ from those who do not in a few categories. These categories include the types of relationship in which they are involved, their goals in relationships and their motivations for having sex.

IDENTIFICATIONS: NAMES/CONCEPTS/TERMS

- Social pressures for condom use
- Perceived ability to use condoms

SAMPLE TEST ITEMS: TRUE/FALSE

1. T F A greater proportion of women than of men had ever had casual sex.

2. T F A greater proportion of women than of men had ever had unprotected sex.

3. T F Respondents who had never had casual sex were more inclined to seek intimacy in relationships.

4. T   F   Women who used condoms consistently were more confident that they could use condoms in difficult situations such as while drunk or when their partner does not want to.

MULTIPLE CHOICE

1. In the study, one of the most common reasons given why a condom was not used was because of:
   a. being too drunk to put a condom on.
   b. not having a condom handy.
   c. not knowing how to put a condom on correctly.
   d. knowing a partner for a long time.
   e. the perception that they are not likely to get pregnant or get an STD.

2. For both men and women, consistent condom use is correlated with:
   a. Having a more positive attitude about condoms.
   b. Perceiving greater social pressure to use condoms.
   c. Having sex to express love.
   d. All of the above.
   e. None of the above.

DISCUSSION ITEM

This study on teen condom use and relationship types and motivations was conducted in the Netherlands. Do you think that the results of the study can be extrapolated to teens in America? Why or why not?

STUDY QUESTION

What are the two categories of relationships that the authors of the study examined?

ANSWERS

True/False:
  1. T
  2. F
  3. T
  4. F
  5. T

Multiple Choice:
  1. B
  2. D

CHAPTER 8

Oral Sex among Adolescents:
Is It Sex or Is It Abstinence?

Lisa Remez

SUMMARY

This article looks at the increasing trend of teens, some as young as middle-schoolers, involved in giving and receiving oral sex. Definitions of "sex" and "abstinence", teen's attitudes and motivations, and some of the consequences of this sexual behavior are examined.

IDENTIFICATIONS: NAMES/CONCEPTS/TERMS

- Fellatio
- Cunnilingus
- Perception of risk

SAMPLE TEST ITEMS: TRUE/FALSE

1. T   F   The author claims that STDs, particularly HIV, has fueled interests in examining teen sexual behaviors that do not necessarily lead to pregnancy.

2. T   F   There are clear definitions for teens as to what they consider to be "sex" and what they consider to be "abstinence".

3. T   F   It is unclear among adolescent health professionals whether teens are actually *having* more oral sex or just *talking* about it more openly now than before.

4. T   F   Experts believe that the type of oral sex practiced by young teenagers is overwhelmingly fellatio and not cunnilingus.

5. T   F   HIV is easily passed through oral sex via saliva.

6. T   F   Oral sex is perceived as a sexual activity that is *less* intimate than vaginal intercourse.

MULTIPLE CHOICE

1. Studies conducted over the past few decades about teen sexual activities had largely focused only on:
   a. deep kissing.
   b. oral sex.
   c. anal sex.
   d. vaginal intercourse.
   e. mutual masturbation.

2. The article explained that teens, some as young as 7th graders, are involved in oral sex because of:
   a. Increased messages about AIDS and abstinence.
   b. High levels of sexual imagery in our culture.
   c. Perception of no-risk in oral sex.
   d. Dual-career, overworked parents who are not around.
   e. All of the above.

3. The article asserts that middle-school girls see performing oral sex on guys as a sexual "bargain" because:
   a. they cannot get pregnant from it.
   b. they think they cannot get diseases from it.
   c. they are still virgins.
   d. they feel more in control since it is something they do to boys.
   e. all of the above.

DISCUSSION ITEM

What behaviors do you personally count as "having sex"?

STUDY QUESTION

How did the Clinton sex scandal fuel confusion about the definition of sex?

ANSWERS

True/False:
1. T
2. F
3. T
4. T
5. F
6. T

Multiple Choice:
1. D
2. E
3. E

S E C T I O N

Sexuality Education

CHAPTER 9

A Case for Offering Comprehensive Sexuality Education in the Schools

John P. Elia, Ph.D.

SUMMARY

The author argues a case for offering comprehensive sexuality education in the schools. Elia discusses many central issues about sexuality education, and ultimately arrives at the conclusion that offering a broad-based sexuality education in the schools is imperative. This piece begins by challenging conventional assumptions about sexuality and gender. Then, this chapter explores the multifaceted characteristics of sexuality. What follow are an explication of various traditional notions and practices of sexuality education, and reasons for moving beyond these traditional notions and practices. Next, a philosophical approach to education that accommodates a responsible treatment of sexuality within school settings including a program of sexuality education that would be more inclusive and responsive to the needs of students than the traditional courses is offered. The question of why sexuality education should be undertaken in the schools as opposed to being the responsibility of other agencies addressed. Finally, a discussion of the characteristics essential to teachers of sexuality education is outlined.

IDENTIFICATIONS: NAMES/CONCEPTS/TERMS

- Traditional notions about sexuality and gender
- Biological sex
- Gender
- Michel Foucault
- Jeffrey Weeks
- Bruess and Greenberg
- SIECUS
- Ludwig Wittgenstein
- Comprehensive sexuality education versus Sex education
- Authority addiction
- John Dewey
- Progressive education
- Pragmatism
- Democracy and democratic educational principles
- Health promotion model
- Disease model
- Censorship
- Moral and non-moral aspects of good sex

SAMPLE TEST ITEMS: TRUE/FALSE

1. T   F   The traditional or standard definitions of sexuality do justice to the complexity of the topic.

2. T   F   Bruess and Greenberg (1988) assert that there are four dimensions of sexuality.

3. T   F   Sex education began in the United States during the late 19th and early 20th centuries to teach people to be more liberal about sexual matters.

4. T   F   Sexuality education courses today focus on the socio-cultural aspects of sexuality and not on the biological or medical aspects.

5. T   F   Inevitably, sexuality education involves addressing some aspects of gender.

MULTIPLE CHOICE

1. John Dewey advocated for teachers to:
   a. allow students to be socially active beings and facilitate and guide them
   b. allow any activities to occur in the classroom for true learning to occur
   c. have students sit still in rows and pay attention to a teacher, the authority
   d. make clear to the students that learning was to take place strictly in school
   e. promote students to work on their own to promote self sufficiency

2. In terms of schooling, bisexuals, gays, and lesbians are:
   a. discussed quite a bit in the schools
   b. the main focus of sexuality education today
   c. virtually ignored and bisexual, gay, and lesbian topics are not addressed
   d. never request that school officials make bisexual, gay, & lesbian issues part of the curriculum
   e. none of the above

3. To date, most sexuality educators have used the _____ model of sexuality education.
   a. health promotion
   b. disease
   c. Montessori
   d. Rogerian
   e. Freudian

4. According to Elia, _____ is the most significant threat to sexuality education.
   a. censorship
   b. a shortage of health education teachers
   c. a shortage of biology teachers
   d. a lack of sexuality education media (videos, films, charts, etc.)
   e. the Clinton/Lewinsky Affair

5. SIECUS is:
   a. a right-wing organization that continues to strive to put sexuality education out of business
   b. a pro abstinence-only sexuality education organization
   c. the name of a sexuality education group in Sweden
   d. a special task force developed three years ago to investigate how much obscenity is a part of sexuality education efforts nationwide
   e. a national organization committed to lobbying for comprehensive sexuality education

DISCUSSION ITEMS

Discuss the differences between comprehensive sexuality education and sex education.

Why is it important to have an expanded conception of sexuality and gender when teaching about sexual matters?

How can studying human sexuality offer more fruitful ways of studying traditional subjects (biology, English, history, social studies, etc.)?

STUDY QUESTIONS

What are the differences of moral and non-moral "good sex"?

Identify some democratic principles that are central to offering comprehensive sexuality education.

List and discuss the characteristics essential for sexuality education teachers.

ANSWERS

True/False:

1. F

2. T

3. F

4. F

5. T

Multiple Choice:

1. A

2. C

3. B

4. A

5. E

C H A P T E R 10

Facts in Brief: Sexuality Education

Alan Guttmacher Institute

SUMMARY

This fact sheet summarizes teen sexual activity and pregnancy, the need for sexuality education, and the different kinds of sexuality education that are being taught in the classroom.

IDENTIFICATIONS: NAMES/CONCEPTS/TERMS

- Abstinence only sex education
- Comprehensive sexuality health education

SAMPLE TEST ITEMS: TRUE/FALSE

1. T F A sexually active teenager who does not use contraception has a 90% chance of becoming pregnant within a year.

2. T F The majority of teen pregnancies are intended, not accidental.

3. T F Though the majority of public school districts are required to teach students sexuality education, what the actual program includes can vary dramatically from school to school.

4. T   F   The majority of American parents want abstinence-only sex education for their children.

5. T   F   Federal laws dictating abstinence-only sex education requires programs to teach that "sexual activity outside of marriage is wrong and harmful", even though this is not medically true.

MULTIPLE CHOICE

1. Every year, there are about 4 million new teenage cases of STDs, especially in _____ infections.
   a. HIV
   b. chlamydia
   c. genital herpes
   d. human papilloma virus
   e. syphilis

2. The majority of teachers believe that information about birth control, condom use, and abortion issues should be taught by:
   a. the end of 6th grade.
   b. the end of 8th grade.
   c. the end of 10th grade.
   d. the end of the 12th grade.
   e. the 1st semester of freshman year of college.

DISCUSSION ITEMS

What kind of sex education did you receive in middle and high school?

Besides formal education at school, where else do kids and teens learn about sexuality?

STUDY QUESTION

What topics do the majority of parents want to see covered in a sexuality education program?

ANSWERS

True/False:
  1. T
  2. F
  3. T
  4. F
  5. T

Multiple Choice:
  1. B
  2. D

C H A P T E R

Issues and Answers: Fact Sheet on Sexuality Education

SIECUS

SUMMARY

This fact sheet is presented in a question and answer format regarding sexuality education. Issues that are discussed include definitions of different kinds of sexuality education, the role of parents in educating kids and teens about sex, the role of schools in offering sex ed programs, and funding by the federal government.

IDENTIFICATIONS: NAMES/CONCEPTS/TERMS

- Teachable moments
- Comprehensive sexuality health education
- Abstinence-based education
- Abstinence-only education
- Abstinence-only-until-marriage education
- Parent-teen communication
- "Virginity Pledges"

SAMPLE TEST ITEMS: TRUE/FALSE

1. T   F   Though a study had shown that almost all parents had talked to their teens about sexuality, only a small percentage felt that parents truly communicated adequately with their teens about sex.

2. T   F   Though parents claimed to have talked with their kids about sexuality topics, a large percentage of the kids (36%–59%) do not recall the conversation.

3. T   F   A study showed that there's no correlation to parent-teen communication about sex and condom usage by the teen.

4. T   F   Abstinence-only sex education programs do not include any information about disease prevention methods.

5. T   F   Sex education programs that include information on contraception has been shown to encourage teens to begin having intercourse earlier than students who were only given information on abstinence.

6. T   F   A study found that young people who took a virginity pledge were less likely to use birth control when they did become sexually active.

MULTIPLE CHOICE

1. Who does SIECUS advocate to be the primary sexuality educators of children?
   a. parents
   b. schools
   c. mass media
   d. religious institutions
   e. peers

2. A study revealed that most parents do not speak to their children about all of the following topics *except:*
   a. Pornography.
   b. Abortion.
   c. Masturbation.
   d. Prostitution.
   e. Dating relationships.

3. The main goal of a comprehensive sexuality education program is:
  a. to provide accurate information about sexuality.
  b. to provide an opportunity for young people to develop their sexual values.
  c. to help young people develop relationship skills.
  d. to help young people exercise responsibility in sexual relationships including decisions about becoming sexually active and use of contraception.
  e. all of the above.

DISCUSSION ITEMS

Do you think that getting students to sign pledges to remain virgins until they are married is reasonable or an effective way to prevent teen pregnancy?

STUDY QUESTIONS

What is the definition of a "teachable moment"?

Name three of the eight definitions that an abstinence-only education program must adhere to in order to receive federal funding.

ANSWERS

True/False:
1. T
2. T
3. F
4. T
5. F
6. T

Multiple Choice:
1. A
2. E
3. E

SECTION **IV**

Sexual Preference

C H A P T E R

The Necessity of Addressing Sexual Identity in the Schools

John P. Elia, Ph.D.

SUMMARY

This chapter addresses why it is so crucial to not only include sexual identity issues in schooling but also to make them central to the entire curriculum. Included in this essay are: a general critique of public schooling in the United States, a description of how schools have been negligent in terms of covering issues of sexual identity in the curriculum, and it concludes with an argument about why this must be covered in schools for purposes of avoiding personal and social harm, building more harmonious relationships and communities, and strengthening the commitment to a democratic and more meaningful education for all students.

IDENTIFICATIONS: NAMES/CONCEPTS/TERMS

- Sexual identity (bisexuality, heterosexuality, & homosexuality)
- "3Rs" curriculum
- Comprehensive sexuality education
- SIECUS National Guidelines Task Force
- Democratic education
- Personal harm
- Social harm

- Biphobia
- Homophobia
- School failure
- Arnstine
- Noddings
- Bruner
- Heterosexism

SAMPLE TEST ITEMS: TRUE/FALSE

1. T   F   Most school administrators are more concerned with academic achievement than the personal welfare of students.

2. T   F   Due to various political and personal views, offering comprehensive sexuality education in the schools has been relatively easy and has not had much opposition.

3. T   F   Discussions of bisexuality and homosexuality happen freely in schools.

4. T   F   Some people argue that because bisexuals, gays and lesbians comprise such a small percentage of the school population, their sexualities should not be discussed.

5. T   F   Bisexuals, gays, and lesbians are all sexual minorities; therefore, there are no misunderstandings or fights between these groups of people.

MULTIPLE CHOICE

1. Just two years ago, the SIECUS National Guidelines Task Force reported that _____ percent of the nation's youth receive comprehensive sexuality education.
   a. 5
   b. 8
   c. 10
   d. 12
   e. 15

2. Specifically regarding the issue of sexual identity, schooling:
   a. covered more about sexual identity in years past compared to now
   b. covers issues about bisexuality but not homosexuality
   c. covers issues about homosexuality but not bisexuality
   d. covers issues pertaining to homosexuality but not heterosexuality
   e. has been unkind, inequitable, and unethical to students

3. According to Elia, keeping bisexual, gay, and lesbian issues closeted in schools:
   a. will make the issue of sexual identity less important
   b. will create a new brand of heterophobia
   c. will feed mistrust, fear, mysteriousness, and hatred of non-heterosexuals
   d. will make bisexuals, gays, and lesbians turn on their teachers
   e. will make it easier for straight students to get along with non-queer peers

4. Elia maintains that:
   a. homosexuality should be discussed more than bisexuality in school settings
   b. heterosexual students ought to be ignored for once
   c. heterosexual students should be shamed into respecting queer people
   d. caring about students as individuals must share a high priority
   e. queer issues should not be raised until high school

5. Arnstine (1995) asserts that diversity:
   a. is a real liability when it comes to educating the young
   b. is a help and not an obstacle when it comes to education
   c. is necessary for any learning to take place
   d. is important in urban schools but not in rural ones
   e. of sexual identity among any student body detracts from academics

DISCUSSION ITEMS

Reflect upon your school days, and identify how your teachers could have addressed issues of sexual identity.

Discuss the importance of covering sexual identity issues in school in terms of not creating personal and social harm.

STUDY QUESTIONS

Identify arguments of those who oppose addressing sexual identity issues in school, and argue against their positions by offering solid reasons for why it is crucial that aspects of sexual identity be addressed in the schools.

Analyze why it is so dangerous, especially for bisexuals, gays, and lesbians, if matters of sexual identity are left out of the schooling process. What are the various consequences?

List the democratic principles that schools might want to endorse to get people to work together in as positive and humane way as possible.

ANSWERS

True/False:
  1. T
  2. F
  3. F
  4. T
  5. F

Multiple Choice:
  1. A
  2. E
  3. C
  4. D
  5. B

CHAPTER 13

Mistakes That Heterosexual People Make When Trying to Appear Non-Prejudiced: The View from LGB People

Terri D. Conley, Ph.D
Christopher Calhoun, B.A.
Sophia R. Evett, Ph.D
Patricia G. Devine, Ph.D

SUMMARY

It is understood people with homophobic and anti-queer views will likely harbor negative stereotypes and prejudicial attitudes toward lesbians, gays, and bisexuals. However, studies show heterosexuals having tolerant views toward homosexuals and bisexuals may also act in negatively prejudicial ways. This article examines the negative behaviors heterosexuals make when interacting with gays, lesbians and bisexuals. Relying on queer stereotypes, using subtle prejudicial language, and not admitting discomfort with queer issues were common "mistakes" heterosexuals make when interacting with homosexual and bisexual men and women.

IDENTIFICATIONS: NAMES/CONCEPTS/TERMS

- Intergroup relationships
- Minority perspectives
- Out-group homogeneity

SAMPLE TEST ITEMS: TRUE/FALSE

1. T   F   Out-group homogeneity relates to the assumption that all gay people are alike.

2. T   F   Family members may be the main perpetrators of making mistakes to appear non-prejudiced toward homosexuals.

3. T   F   Homosexual and bisexual people who believe others were aware of their sexual orientation were less receptive to mistakes made by heterosexuals.

4. T   F   In this study, homosexual men and women had a challenging time identifying and describing the mistakes encountered by heterosexual people.

5. T   F   The study concluded that to appear non-prejudiced toward gay, lesbian and bisexual people heterosexuals must strike a balance between paying too much attention and too little attention to the topic of homosexuality when in the presence of homosexual and bisexual men and women.

MULTIPLE CHOICE

1. The respondents in the study concluded a common mistake heterosexuals made when trying to appear non-prejudiced toward homosexuals was:
   a. Stating they know someone who is gay or lesbian
   b. Stating they wish their children were gay or lesbian
   c. Stating an attraction for someone of the same gender
   d. Admitting to having some discomfort with homosexuality issues
   e. Pointing out directly that they are not prejudiced toward homosexuals

2. Which of the following was NOT a common mistake people made when trying to appear non-prejudiced toward homosexual men and women?
   a. Stating that they know another homosexual person
   b. Using subtle prejudicial language
   c. Asking inappropriate or too many questions
   d. Ignoring or avoiding the topic of homosexuality
   e. Stating a desire to engage in sex with someone of the same gender

3. Which of the following was NOT shown to influence how a homosexual person perceived the mistakes made by heterosexuals?
   a. Age
   b. Gender
   c. Family support
   d. Virginity status (virgin or non-virgin)
   e. Being "out" or "closeted"

4. Which of the following is TRUE regarding how homosexuals identify the mistakes heterosexuals make when trying to be non-prejudiced?
   a. Homosexual people have difficulty identifying the mistakes
   b. Homosexual people are quite able to identify the mistakes
   c. Older homosexual women are least likely to identify the mistakes
   d. Younger homosexual women are most likely to identify the mistakes
   e. Older homosexual men are least likely to identify the mistakes

5. From the study, when homosexual men and women believed others knew about their sexual orientation they were:
   a. Most receptive to identifying heterosexuals' mistakes
   b. Equally receptive to identifying heterosexuals' mistakes
   c. Less receptive to identifying heterosexuals' mistakes
   d. More receptive to identifying only family members' mistakes
   e. More receptive to identifying only family members' and friends' mistakes

DISCUSSION ITEMS

What mistakes have you and/or someone else made in attempting to be non-prejudiced toward homosexual and bisexual men and women?

What do you feel are the common mistakes people make when trying to be non-prejudiced toward homosexual and bisexual men and women?

STUDY QUESTIONS

What are the mistakes heterosexual people make when trying to appear non-prejudiced? How does a homosexual person's age and gender affect his/her perception of these mistakes?

How does family support or lack of support influence a homosexual person's perception of mistakes heterosexuals make to appear non-prejudiced?

ANSWERS

True/False:

1. T
2. T
3. T
4. F
5. T

Multiple Choice:

1. A
2. E
3. D
4. B
5. C

C H A P T E R

Fact Sheet: Lesbian, Gay, Bisexual, and Transgendered Youth Issues

SIECUS

SUMMARY

This fact sheet contains statistics regarding sexual identity and orientation, contraceptive use, HIV risk, harassment, sexual abuse, substance use, suicide and more of lesbian, gay, bisexual and transgendered youth.

IDENTIFICATIONS: NAMES/CONCEPTS/TERMS

- LGBT
- Homophobia

SAMPLE TEST ITEMS: TRUE/FALSE

1. T   F   The amount of uncertainty about one's sexual orientation seems to remain the same from early adolescence (age 12) to late adolescence (age 17).

2. T   F   A study of high school students (9th–12th graders) found a correlation between gay/lesbian/bisexual orientation and having had sexual intercourse before age 13, often against one's will.

3. T   F   A study of 9th–12th graders found that gay, lesbian, and bisexual youth were five times as likely to report failing to attend school because of their fear about safety.

4. T   F   Teen boys have a much higher rate of sexual abuse than teen girls.

5. T   F   A study of public high school students found that gay and bisexual students have about the same rate of attempted suicides as their heterosexual peers.

MULTIPLE CHOICE

1. One study on HIV risk confirms that _____ act as a "bridge" for HIV transmission to women.
   a. young gay men
   b. young lesbians
   c. young bisexual men
   d. young heterosexual men
   e. older heterosexual men

2. What percentage of LGBTQ youths in one national survey reported hearing homophobic remarks from students?
   a. 25%
   b. 43%
   c. 53%
   d. 75%
   e. 91%

3. When asked, "What is the youngest age you feel you might need to talk to your children about homosexuality?," the highest percentage of parents responded:
   a. Under 5 years old
   b. Age 7–8
   c. Age 9–10
   d. Age 13–14
   e. Age 17–18

4. The majority of high school health teachers (66%) identified _____ as the most commonly used source of information regarding homosexuality.
   a. mass media
   b. parents and other family members
   c. peers
   d. religion
   e. school health education programs

DISCUSSION ITEM

Why do you think that bisexual/lesbian youth have twice the rate of pregnancy than heterosexual young women?

STUDY QUESTIONS

According to the article, what would increase the likelihood of gay and bisexual men getting tested for HIV?

What is the perception of gay and lesbian teens of coming out to friends and getting support?

ANSWERS

True/False:
  1. F
  2. T
  3. T
  4. F
  5. F

Multiple Choice:
  1. C
  2. E
  3. C
  4. A

V

Parenting, Relationships, and Sexual Behavior

CHAPTER 15

The Eight Stages of Ending a Relationship

Albert J. Angelo, MS.Ed.

SUMMARY

In this article, the author highlights eight distinct stages a person experiences when a relationship ends. The process begins with one or both partners denying the relationship is in trouble and continues when attempts are made to "fix" the problems. If the relationship cannot be maintained, feelings of grief and loss result. The process is finalized when one feels at peace for being able to let go of both the hope and the hurt. As the author states, by working through the eight stages one becomes better prepared to fully love again.

IDENTIFICATIONS: NAMES/CONCEPTS/TERMS

- Denial
- Anger/Confusion
- We Can Work it Out
- It's Over: Now to Grieve
- What Went Wrong
- I'm Not the Same Person
- No Going Back
- Peace

- Obsession
- Bargaining
- Regrets
- Pleasant Surprise

SAMPLE TEST ITEMS: TRUE/FALSE

1. T   F   Both partners will feel "Pleasant Surprise" sometime within the first two stages of an ending relationship.

2. T   F   Only the partner being left will experience "Bargaining."

3. T   F   The partner choosing to end the relationship may feel "Regret."

4. T   F   A person will likely experience tremendous anger during the "No Going Back" stage.

5. T   F   The stage "I'm Not the Same Person" comes before the stage "We Can Work it Out."

MULTIPLE CHOICE

1. The first stage a person experiences during an ending relationship is:
   a. Anger
   b. Unexpected relief
   c. Frustration
   d. Resentment
   e. Denial

2. Which statement is true regarding the stages of an ending relationship?
   a. Only one partner will experience "Peace"
   b. Both partners will go through each of the stages at the same time
   c. The stage of "anger" comes near the end of the grieving process
   d. Only the partner ending the relationship will experience anger
   e. Both partners will pass through the "We Can Work it Out" stage

3. The last stage of an ending relationship is:
   a. Harmony
   b. Regret
   c. Anger
   d. Peace
   e. Depression

4. "Bargaining" and "Obsession" can occur during which stage of an ending relationship?
   a. Denial
   b. Peace
   c. We Can Work it Out
   d. What Went Wrong
   e. No Going Back

5. "Regrets" and "Pleasant Surprise" occur during which stage?
   a. What Went Wrong
   b. We Can Work it Out
   c. Peace
   d. Denial
   e. Anger/Confusion

DISCUSSION ITEMS

Does gender, age, ethnicity, and sexual orientation influence how one experiences the stages of an ending relationship? If so, how?

Is friendship possible when a relationship ends?

STUDY QUESTIONS

How is the "We Can Work it Out" stage different from the "What Went Wrong" stage?

How is "Bargaining" different from "Obsession?"

ANSWERS

True/False:

1. F

2. F

3. T

4. F

5. F

Multiple Choice:

1. E

2. E

3. D

4. C

5. A

CHAPTER 16

Sperm Donors Meet Their Families

Linda Villarosa

SUMMARY

This article discusses the increasing trend of sperm donor usage and of donors meeting children that were produced by their sperm. The experiences of donors, parents who have used donor sperm, and children resulting from those sperm are shared.

IDENTIFICATIONS: NAMES/CONCEPTS/TERMS

- Donor identification release
- Assisted reproductive technology
- Intracytoplasmic sperm injection

SAMPLE TEST ITEMS: TRUE/FALSE

1. T   F   In the past, families who had used sperm donors to conceive were counseled to never disclose that fact to other people.

2. T   F   Bob, a sperm donor profiled in the article, was so overjoyed with meeting his biological daughter that he would like to meet other children that may have been formed with his sperm.

3. T   F   The donor identification release program for sperm donors is modeled after adoption programs that release identification of biological parents.

MULTIPLE CHOICE

1. In the past, clients of sperm banks were overwhelmingly:
   a. Lesbians
   b. Infertile married couples
   c. Single young women
   d. Gay male couples using a surrogate
   e. Elderly women

2. What medical procedure sharply increased fertility among couples with male infertility issues?
   a. Zygote intra-Fallopian transfer
   b. In-vitro fertilization
   c. Gamete intra-Fallopian transfer
   d. Intracytoplasmic sperm injection
   e. Artificial insemination

3. In the 1990s and 2000s, the *fastest growing* population/s to use sperm donation is/are:
   a. Lesbians
   b. Infertile married couples
   c. Single women
   d. A and B
   e. A and C

DISCUSSION ITEMS

Would you ever donate your sperm or eggs? Why or why not?

If you were to donate your sperm or eggs, would you want to meet the children that were produced from those sperm or eggs? Why or why not?

STUDY QUESTIONS

If a sperm donor agrees to sign a donor identification release, what is he agreeing to do?

In the past, why were heterosexual couples told not to tell anyone that they had used a sperm donor?

ANSWERS

True/False:
   1. T
   2. F
   3. T

Multiple Choice:
   1. B
   2. D
   3. E

C H A P T E R **17**

The Ambiguity of "Having Sex": The Subjective Experience of Virginity Loss in the United States

---

Laura M. Carpenter

SUMMARY

Defining what behaviors constitute the "loss" of one's virginity is extremely challenging. Variables such as age, gender, sexual orientation, culture, and lifestyle practices influence our interpretations. This article examines how young men and women interpret virginity loss and what specific sexual behaviors they believe cause and do not cause one to lose his or her virginity.

IDENTIFICATIONS: NAMES/CONCEPTS/TERMS

- Virginity loss
- Virgin and nonvirgin
- Social identity
- Personal identity
- Technical virginity

SAMPLE TEST ITEMS: TRUE/FALSE

1. T   F   The term "technical virgin" can only be applied to homosexual males and females.

2. T   F   Most participants in this study believed men and women could lose their virginity with a same-sex partner.

3. T   F   All gay male participants in this study believed being a virgin was not a stigma.

4. T   F   From a policy prospective, the author argues that schools should promote abstinence education to encourage young men and women to remain virgins.

5. T   F   The author believes defining the term "sex" is easier than defining the term "virginity".

MULTIPLE CHOICE

1. In which decade did young American women increasingly approve of engaging in premarital sexual intercourse with partners they did not expect to marry?
a. 1890s
b. 1920s
c. 1940s
d. 1950s
e. 1960s

2. The author states research participants in her study completely agreed that virginity loss includes:
a. Oral sex performed on a man by a woman
b. Oral sex performed on a woman by a man
c. Anal intercourse between two men
d. Anal intercourse between a man to a woman
e. Heterosexual vaginal intercourse

3. The author believes virginity loss is almost universally recognized as:
a. A horrible event for women but not for men
b. A horrible event for adolescent men and women
c. An important right of passage
d. A horrible event for adolescent women but not for adolescent men
e. A horrible event for men but not for women

4. "Technical virginity" equates virginity loss with this activity:
a. Anal sex between a man and a woman
b. Anal sex between two men
c. Any form of anal or vaginal intercourse
d. Oral sex between two women
e. Vaginal intercourse between a man and a woman

5. From the article, which of the following is true?
  a. More young women than young men view virginity as a gift and not a stigma
  b. More young men than young women view virginity as a gift and not a stigma
  c. More young men than young women believe anal sex is not "real sex"
  d. Almost all young women believe anal sex is not "real sex"
  e. Almost all young men believe anal sex is not "real sex"

DISCUSSION ITEMS

How do you define "virginity" and what behaviors do you believe cause one to "lose" his or her virginity?

Can a person lose his or her virginity by engaging in sex with a same-gender partner? Why or why not?

STUDY QUESTIONS

What does it mean to be a "technical virgin?"

How does "social identity" and "personal identity" influence one's perception of being a virgin or nonvirgin?

ANSWERS

True/False:

1. F
2. T
3. F
4. F
5. F

Multiple Choice:

1. E
2. E
3. C
4. E
5. A

CHAPTER 18

Conceptual Models of Sexual Activity

Al Vernacchio, M.S.Ed.

SUMMARY

This article explores the connection between a conceptual model of sexual activity and how that model guides sexual behavior. The author suggests that the primary conceptual model used for sexual activity in American society today is baseball. That is, we use baseball terminology, and the rules and structure of a baseball game to think about and explain what sexual activity should be like. After reviewing some common baseball-related terminology and how it relates to sexual activity, the author argues that a conceptual model for sexual activity based on baseball leads to sexual activity and relationships that are unfulfilling, restrictive and inequitable. This is done first by examining the concept of baseball and then by applying that concept to sexual activity. An alternative conceptual model, based on the idea of pizza is offered. By first examining the concept of pizza and then applying it to sexual activity, it is argued that using pizza as a conceptual model for sexual activity may result in sexual activity and relationships that are more equitable, flexible, and fulfilling.

IDENTIFICATIONS: NAMES/CONCEPTS/TERMS

- conceptual model
- baseball model/pizza model

- "pitcher"/"catcher"
- "bench warmer"
- "switch-hitter"/"plays for the other team"
- "bat"/"nappy dugout"

SAMPLE TEST ITEMS: TRUE/FALSE

1. T   F   Deborah Roffman argues that the baseball metaphor helps to transmit healthy and helpful messages about sexual activity.

2. T   F   In baseball-related terminology for sexuality, a "glove" or "catcher's mitt" refers to a condom.

3. T   F   The baseball-based conceptual model for sexual activity is sexist because it assumes that the man is the active partner in sexual activity and the woman is the passive partner.

4. T   F   The pizza-based conceptual model of sexual activity suggests that a specific skill set is needed to adequately perform sexual activity.

5. T   F   A pizza-based conceptual model for sexual activity suggests that sexual activity should result from desire and not obligation or coercion.

MULTIPLE CHOICE

1. According to the baseball model, getting to "second base" is commonly understood to mean:
   a. touching a man's breasts
   b. touching a woman's vulva
   c. touching a man's penis
   d. touching a woman's breasts

2. Using the baseball-related conceptual model for sexual activity, all of the following are true, except:
   a. sexual activity is a competitive, oppositional activity
   b. sexual activity has a strict order
   c. sexual activity requires a specific skill set
   d. sexual activity requires communication and negotiation before activity takes place

3. The baseball-based conceptual model of sexual activity suggests that all of the following groups should "get out of the game" of sexual activity, except:
   a. senior citizens
   b. prostitutes
   c. the disabled
   d. those with chronic illness

4. One of the things that makes using pizza as a conceptual model for sexual activity successful is:
   a. pizza is not very expensive
   b. very few people are allergic to pizza
   c. pizza is universally understood in our culture
   d. pizza is usually associated with a negative experience

5. All of the following are benefits of using a pizza-based conceptual model for sexual activity, except:
   a. it makes sexual activity more structured and goal directed
   b. it establishes the primacy of individual desire and the decisions of the participants as the controlling factors in sexual activity
   c. it opens the participants to a wider range of behaviors that can be expressed
   d. it frees sexual activity from restrictions and external rules

DISCUSSION ITEMS

Where do you find the baseball model at work in our society today? Do you hear people using baseball-related terms to talk about sexual activity? Do you hear people referencing baseball-related concepts when describing sexual activity? How does the Media use the baseball model when it presents ideas about sexual activity?

Do you feel influenced by the baseball model? Do you find your own thoughts, words, or actions related to sexual activity influenced by the baseball-based conceptual model?

STUDY QUESTIONS

The author argues that baseball related terminology about sexual activity is both sexist and homophobic. Explain how.

What are the four questions someone can ask to see if they are influenced by the baseball conceptual model of sexual activity?

ANSWERS

True/False:
1. F
2. T
3. T
4. F
5. T

Multiple Choice:
1. D
2. D
3. B
4. C
5. A

Sexual Health, Aging, Sexual Victimization, and Disabilities

C H A P T E R

Facts in Brief: Sexual and Reproductive Health: Men and Women

Alan Guttmacher Institute

SUMMARY

This fact sheet contains statistics regarding sexual activities, contraceptive use, sexually transmitted infections, abortion, pregnancy and parenting, marriage and sexual/reproductive health services.

IDENTIFICATIONS: NAMES/CONCEPTS/TERMS

- Vasectomy
- Medicaid
- Sexual and reproductive health "service set"

SAMPLE TEST ITEMS: TRUE/FALSE

1. T   F   Men, on average, are sexually active for nearly 10 years before getting married.

2. T   F   Most adults in their 30s and 40s have more than one sexual partner in the past year.

3. T   F   At all ages, women are more likely than men to contract genital herpes, chlamydia, or gonorrhea.

4. T   F   One of the fastest growing population of new HIV infections is heterosexual women.

5. T   F   Most abortions involve people in the teens.

MULTIPLE CHOICE

1. The majority of adolescents, male and female, used the _____ as their method of birth control the first time they had intercourse.
   a. birth control pill
   b. male condom
   c. diaphragm
   d. birth control patch
   e. nothing

2. Half of women have had a child by age _____.
   a. 18
   b. 22
   c. 24
   d. 26
   e. 30

3. What percentage of men have no health insurance in their 20s?
   a. 20%
   b. 40%
   c. 50%
   d. 70%
   e. 80%

DISCUSSION ITEM

Why do you think that condom use declines as men and women get older?

STUDY QUESTIONS

According to the article, why is it that more men are married in the 40s than women in their 40s?

Why is it that adult men are less likely to get sexual/reproductive health care services than adult women?

ANSWERS

True/False:
 1. T
 2. F
 3. T
 4. T
 5. F

Multiple Choice:
 1. B
 2. D
 3. B

CHAPTER 20

The Young Men's Clinic: Addressing Men's Reproductive Health and Responsibilities

Bruce Armstrong

SUMMARY

This report examines the Young Men's Clinic in New York City as a model to provide adolescent and young adult men with the sexual and reproductive health care services that they need.

IDENTIFICATIONS: NAMES/CONCEPTS/TERMS

- Key informants
- Teachable moments
- Empowerment

SAMPLE TEST ITEMS: TRUE/FALSE

1. T F   Part of the success in getting men to visit the clinic is by incorporating other activities such as basketball and break dancing to clinic visits.

2. T F   Focus groups with "key informants" in the community such as high school football coaches and clergy gave crucial information about the types of sexual and reproductive health care services that young men needed.

3. T   F   Mental health care services are also currently being provided at the clinic.

4. T   F   The Men's Clinic is decorated the same as most women's clinics.

MULTIPLE CHOICE

1. The clientele served at the Men's Clinic in New York City was primarily:
   a. white.
   b. black.
   c. Hispanic.
   d. Asian.
   e. American Indian.

2. Young men claim that certain barriers prevent them from visiting a men's clinic including:
   a. Being seen by someone they know.
   b. Admitting that they are sexually active.
   c. The perception that clinics are for women only.
   d. The belief that talking about birth control is not "manly".
   e. All of the above.

DISCUSSION ITEM

What are some of the sexual issues that you think young men have?

STUDY QUESTIONS

Describe one of the outreach programs that are being done to promote the Young Men's Clinic

How has the Young Men's Clinic been funded?

ANSWERS

True/False:
1. T
2. T
3. F
4. F

Multiple Choice:
1. C
2. E

C H A P T E R

21

HIV/AIDS Diagnosis

National Women's Health Resource Center

SUMMARY

The article goes over the different kinds of HIV tests that are available, including some of the older blood tests and some of the newer methods like the oral test, the rapid antibody test and the home tests.

IDENTIFICATIONS: NAMES/CONCEPTS/TERMS

- Enzyme Immunosrobent Assay (EIA)
- Western Blot (WB)
- Immunofluorescence Assay (IFA)
- Antibodies
- Seroconversion
- Rapid antibody test
- Orasure

SAMPLE TEST ITEMS: TRUE/FALSE

1. T   F   The EIA test detects the actual HIV virus in the infected person's blood.

2. T   F   If an HIV test result is "positive", it means that the person is not infected.

3. T   F   When an EIA test detects an HIV infection, the same test is repeated and then confirmed with another type of test such as the Western Blot or an Immunofluorescence Assay.

4. T   F   The Orasure test, which uses a treated cotton pad to collect oral fluids, is just as accurate as a blood test.

MULTIPLE CHOICE

1. The "window period" between actual infection and the production of HIV antibodies usually last up to:
   a. 2 weeks.
   b. 1 month.
   c. 3 months.
   d. 6 months.
   e. 1 year.

2. According to the article, HIV-infected women are more likely than non-HIV-infected women to have:
   a. Genital herpes.
   b. Fibrous breasts changes.
   c. Ovarian cysts.
   d. Endometriosis.
   e. Abnormal Pap smears.

DISCUSSION ITEMS

What do you think are some of the benefits of the rapid antibody test, which can provide results in 20 minutes?

What do you think are some of the advantages and disadvantages of an HIV home test?

STUDY QUESTION

How exactly is the HIV home test done?

ANSWERS

True/False:
  1. F
  2. F
  3. T
  4. T

Multiple Choice:
  1. C
  2. E

C H A P T E R 22

A Genuine Feel-Good Story:
Sex May Help Prevent Prostate Cancer

Carl T. Hall

SUMMARY

A new study has found that frequent sexual activity may decrease the risk of developing prostate cancer, contrary to some older research.

IDENTIFICATIONS: NAMES/CONCEPTS/TERMS

- Prostate gland
- Ejaculation
- Semen

SAMPLE TEST ITEMS: TRUE/FALSE

1. T F The study involved men between the age of 18–35, the age group with the highest risk of prostate cancer.

2. T F Prostate cancer is the most common kind of cancer in men.

3. T F The theory behind the results was that frequent ejaculations help to flush out cancer-causing chemicals.

MULTIPLE CHOICE

1. Past research suggested that frequent sex increased men's risk for prostate cancer by:
   a. Not allowing the prostate to rest enough between ejaculations.
   b. The performance of certain sexual behaviors that damaged the prostate.
   c. Overworking the prostate to continually produce seminal fluids.
   d. Physical pressures that are put on the prostate while having sex.
   e. Exposing men to various germs and viruses that lead to prostate cancer.

2. Men who are _____ have the highest chances of prostate cancer.
   a. white
   b. black
   c. Latino
   d. Asian/pacific islander
   e. American Indian

3. Having _____ ejaculation/s a month were linked with decreased cancer risk:
   a. 1
   b. 3–5
   c. 5–8
   d. 9–12
   e. 13–20

DISCUSSION ITEM

What are some problems with men accessing sexual health services, including screening for prostate cancer?

STUDY QUESTIONS

On average, how often did the men who participated in the study ejaculate in a month?

How many estimated new cases of prostate cancer are expected to be diagnosed in a year and how many men will die from prostate cancer in a year?

ANSWERS

True/False:
1. F
2. F
3. T

Multiple Choice:
1. E
2. B
3. E

CHAPTER 23

Whatever Happened to June Cleaver?
The Fifties Mom Turns Eighty

Laura Katz Olson
Political Science
Lehigh University

SUMMARY

During the 1950's American women were socially and institutionally denied occupational and financial equality. Employment opportunities available to women consisted mostly of low-paying jobs with little or no benefits or potential for advancement. The author examines how the current financial health of these women, who are now in their 80s and are living in poverty or near-poverty conditions, is a result of unequal opportunities and unequal gender roles inherent in 1950s America.

IDENTIFICATIONS: NAMES/CONCEPTS/TERMS

- Nuclear family
- Pink-collar work
- Racism
- Social Security

SAMPLE TEST ITEMS: TRUE/FALSE

1. T   F   Female employment increased during the 1950s.

2. T   F   In 1959, the working wages of women was 61% that of men.

3. T   F   In the 1950s African American women were expected to work in order to support themselves and their families.

4. T   F   Currently, most elderly women collect Social Security benefits based on their husbands' wage records.

5. T   F   A majority of older widowed women rely on their husbands' Social Security benefits for most or all of their financial support.

MULTIPLE CHOICE

1. Which group was the *lowest* paid employees during the 1950s:
   a. White women
   b. African American men
   c. White men
   d. African American women
   e. Asian men

2. Social Security benefit levels are based on these two criteria:
   a. Wages and ethnicity
   b. Wages and number of years worked
   c. Gender and marital status
   d. Gender and ethnicity
   e. Ethnicity and marital status

3. Which of the following was NOT mentioned as a method to strengthen the financial integrity of the Social Security system:
   a. Lower the retirement age for single women
   b. Raise the retirement age for single women
   c. Raise the retirement age for married women
   d. Raise payroll taxes for single women
   e. Raise payroll taxes for married women

4. June Cleaver is:
   a. A former political leader of the National Organization of Women
   b. A former political supporter of the Equal Rights Amendment
   c. A TV character of a 1950s housewife
   d. The current president of Planned Parenthood
   e. The former Treasury Secretary under the Clinton Administration

5. When World War II ended, most women working in the factories were:
   a. Encouraged to quit or were fired
   b. Promoted to management-level positions
   c. Paid equally to newly hired men
   d. Encouraged to earn college degrees
   e. Paid more than newly hired men

DISCUSSION ITEMS

In today's society are job opportunities and wages equal for men and women? If not, why?

How are current male and female gender roles similar to and different from those in the 1950s?

STUDY QUESTIONS

Today, many older American women live in poverty or near-poverty conditions. How did gender roles, laws, institutions, and cultural influences in the 1950s encourage this outcome?

How did racism affect the economic conditions of African American women in the 1950s? How were the lives of African American women similar to and different from white women?

ANSWERS

True/False:
1. T
2. T
3. T
4. T
5. T

Multiple Choice:
1. D
2. B
3. A
4. C
5. A

CHAPTER 24

Sex Offenders: Myths and Facts

Catherine Piliero-Surbeck, Ph.D.

SUMMARY

In this article, the author dispels the myths and articulates the facts about sexual offenders. Some commonly held misperceptions include the belief that all sexual offenders are male, mentally deficient, and easily identifiable. The facts about sexual offenders include family histories of sexual and emotional abuse, denial of their abusive behavior, and feeling a lack of empathy for their victims. Treatment options are discussed including relapse prevention, covert sensitization, and victim empathy.

IDENTIFICATIONS: NAMES/CONCEPTS/TERMS

- Arousal re-conditioning
- "Buttering up phase"
- Covert sensitization
- "Cruising"
- "Grooming"
- Post-assault phase
- Relapse prevention
- Sex crimes

- Sex offender
- Sexual aggression
- Victim empathy

SAMPLE TEST ITEMS: TRUE/FALSE

1. T   F   There is no cure for sex offenders.

2. T   F   It is uncommon for males to be sexually abused by sex offenders.

3. T   F   Rape is not an act of sex but only of violence.

4. T   F   Many sex offenders aggressively deny their offenses when caught.

5. T   F   Most victims of sexual offenses know their offender.

MULTIPLE CHOICE

1. Which is NOT a treatment option for sex offenders:
   a. manipulation conditioning
   b. relapse prevention
   c. covert sensitization
   d. victim empathy
   e. arousal re-conditioning

2. Which drug has been used to treat sex offenders:
   a. sporonox
   b. DHEA
   c. interconozol
   d. dipanzonol
   e. depo provera

3. "Grooming" a victim means:
   a. raping a victim
   b. physically abusing a victim
   c. preparing a victim for sexual assault
   d. murdering a victim
   e. apologizing to a victim

4. "Cruising" a victim means:
   a. physically abusing a victim
   b. raping a victim
   c. locating a victim
   d. murdering a victim
   e. driving a victim away from his/her home

5. During the "post-assault" phase, a sex offender will likely:
   a. feel guilt for committing the sexual assault
   b. fantasize about the sexual assault
   c. confess to the sexual assault
   d. apologize to the victim of the sexual assault
   e. feel sad for committing the sexual assault

DISCUSSION ITEMS

How can we as individuals and as a society help reduce the prevalence of sexual offenses?

How would you educate and protect children against sexual offenders?

STUDY QUESTIONS

What are the various treatments for sex offenders described in this article and how do they work?

What are the myths and facts regarding sex offenders? What characteristics do sex offenders often share?

ANSWERS

True/False:

1. T
2. F
3. F
4. T
5. T

Multiple Choice:

1. A
2. E
3. C
4. C
5. B

CHAPTER 25

Complexities of Discussing the Erotic Lives of People with Disabilities

Sandy O'Neill, Ph.D. (cand.)

SUMMARY

This chapter offers a much needed coverage of sexuality and disability. The author poses the following questions: What is a disability? How can we define people with disabilities? What is a disability studies/disability rights perspective? What types of societal conceptions and/or misconceptions about the expectations of people with disabilities might shape our ideas about them/us? Are people with disabilities culturally perceived as being asexual (non and/or under interested in sex) or being oversexed? Which stereotypes about disabled people effect views on their/our sexuality? And, what is it that mandates including discussions of disability issues in human sexuality texts and courses? How does including people with disabilities in thinking about sex change notions of sexuality and the erotic? In addition to providing detailed and thoughtful responses to each of the above-mentioned questions, O'Neill provides a critique of the ways people with disabilities are portrayed in human sexuality textbooks. She discusses many of the salient issues surrounding sexuality and disability and challenges the prevailing myths and stereotypes from a disability rights perspective. O'Neill does much to set the record straight!

IDENTIFICATIONS: NAMES/CONCEPTS/TERMS

- Ableism
- Disability rights
- Physical disabilities
- Developmental disabilities
- Emotional disabilities
- Americans with Disabilities Act
- Oppression
- Abasiophilia
- Eugenics
- Social hygiene
- Havelock Ellis

SAMPLE TEST ITEMS: TRUE/FALSE

1. T   F   Only those with physical disabilities are viewed as being either asexual or oversexed.

2. T   F   In the United States, we are immersed in a culture that diagnoses and medicalizes an increasing number of problems. The Americans with Disabilities Act has remedied all physical and emotional barriers that people with disabilities have encountered. Disabled actors are rarely cast in movies or on TV unless the disability is the topic of the show. Abasiophilia is defined as the "love of and sexual attraction to people with psychiatric disabilities.

3. T   F   The Americans with Disabilities Act has remedied all physical and emotional barriers that people with disabilities have encountered.

4. T   F   Disabled actors are rarely cast in movies or on TV unless the disability is the topic of the show.

5. T   F   Abasiophilia is defined as the "love of and sexual attraction to people with psychiatric disabilities."

MULTIPLE CHOICE

1. According to O'Neill, people with disabilities have been tortured, sterilized, and murdered in:
   a. *The Holy Bible*
   b. the coliseum of the Roman Empire
   c. Medieval France
   d. eighteenth-century England
   e. Nazi Germany

2. O'Neill states that our first "common sense" instinct is to characterize people with disabilities as:
   a. sex crazed maniacs
   b. desexualized individuals
   c. too fragile to have sex
   d. into sex toys and other sexual paraphernalia to substitute for human sex partners
   e. sexual beings like to non-disabled population

3. In the past few years, the popular TV show that had two episodes that focused on how easily developmentally or emotionally disabled people can be blamed for murders or sexual assaults of children was:
   a. Three's Company
   b. Home Improvement
   c. NYPD Blue
   d. The Jerry Springer Show
   e. Oprah

4. There have been established categories of paraphilias and fetishes for about:
   a. 100 years
   b. 80 years
   c. 60 years
   d. 40 years
   e. 20 years

5. According to O'Neill, oppression:
   a. has been around for as long as humans have been around
   b. is best studied and written about in a biological context
   c. of disabled people has ironically increased since Americans with Disabilities Act was put into effect
   d. can be unlearned
   e. all of the above

DISCUSSION ITEMS

Discuss how you have or have not reinforced ("gone along with") society's perception of the disabled as either desexualized (non-sexual individuals) or as oversexed people.

Discuss several ways of combating sexual prejudice against, and negative stereotypes about, disabled people.

STUDY QUESTIONS

Identify and analyze why it is so difficult to define disability.

Give examples of how disabled people are portrayed on popular television shows, and write about how you would change such programs to reflect a more positive attitude about disabled individuals. Be specific and provide concrete examples.

Discuss how non-disabled individuals' sexual attraction to disabled people or their appliances (crutches, wheelchairs, and other orthopedic devices) as weird or pathological—even to the extent of having categories of psychiatric diagnoses—is inherently discriminatory toward the disabled, and reinforces a sex negative attitude about them.

ANSWERS

True/False:
  1. F
  2. T
  3. F
  4. T
  5. T

Multiple Choice:
  1. E
  2. B
  3. C
  4. A
  5. D

Sexuality and Spirituality

C H A P T E R **26**

Sexuality and Spirituality: The Relevance of Eastern Traditions

Robert T. Francoeur, Ph.D., ACS

SUMMARY

This article examines sexuality and spirituality according to Eastern traditions. Tantrism and Taoism are discussed and framed within the context of Hinduism and other Eastern religions. The author illustrates how Eastern traditions embrace sexuality and sexual pleasure as positive human experiences and suggests Western culture could benefit from adopting these sex-affirming views.

IDENTIFICATIONS: NAMES/CONCEPTS/TERMS

- Ananga Ranga
- Dharma
- Hinduism
- Kama Sutra
- Rati
- Shiva
- Tantrism
- Taoism
- Vishnu
- Yoga

SAMPLE TEST ITEMS: TRUE/FALSE

1. T   F   Taoist traditions emphasize the importance of female sexual desire and sexual pleasure.

2. T   F   Yoga literally translated from Sanskrit means "calm ejaculation."

3. T   F   Hindu sexual views are associated with mythological figures such as Vishnu and Shiva.

4. T   F   Taoism advocates a life of celibacy and the repression of one's sexual desires and passions.

5. T   F   Taoism encourages men to enhance their sexual ecstasy by learning to control their ejaculations.

MULTIPLE CHOICE

1. According to Taoist beliefs, sexual behavior is:
    a. always sinful in the eyes of God
    b. natural and not sinful
    c. sinful outside of marriage
    d. not sinful but morally unhealthy
    e. sinful unless two people are in love

2. This manual discusses the spiritual aspects of sexuality and the positions and techniques to increase sexual pleasure:
    a. Shiva Manual
    b. Tantric Manual
    c. Rati Sutra
    d. Dharma Manual
    e. Kama Sutra

3. The figure "Vishnu" is associated with this religion:
    a. Hinduism
    b. Christianity
    c. Judaism
    d. Buddhism
    e. Islam

4. In Hinduism, this figure is the embodiment of *sensual* love:
    a. Dharma
    b. Vishnu
    c. Rati
    d. Shiva
    e. Brahma

5. This is the Hindu god of love:
   a. Rati
   b. Shiva
   c. Brahma
   d. Kama
   e. Kali

DISCUSSION ITEMS

How are your views regarding sexuality and sexual behavior similar to or different from those expressed by Eastern traditions? Explain.

Do you feel it would be beneficial if Western culture adopted similar views regarding sexuality as Eastern traditions? Explain.

STUDY QUESTIONS

What is "Taoism?" How do Taoist sexual traditions differ from Western sexual values?

What is "yoga?" How can practicing yoga help enhance one's sexual pleasure?

ANSWERS

True/False:
1. T
2. F
3. T
4. F
5. T

Multiple Choice:
1. B
2. E
3. A
4. C
5. D

SECTION VIII

The Sex Industry and Sex Technology

C H A P T E R

Sex Work: A Contemporary Introduction to the World's Oldest Trade

Carol Queen, Ed. D.

SUMMARY

This chapter discusses a wide range of sex work. The author treats prostitution, peep show work and stripping, porn models and performers, professional dominants, phone and computer sex workers, porn writers, adult industry distribution and retail, surrogate partners, sex educators and therapists, porn crusaders and vice officers, and clients and customers. Queen not only provides descriptions of various types of sex work but also she includes a discussion of research on sex work, historical and legal aspects of the sex industry, international issues, stereotypes about sex works, feminism and sex work, and sex worker rights organizing.

IDENTIFICATIONS: NAMES/CONCEPTS/TERMS

- Sex work
- Sex industry
- Brothels
- Whore of Babylon
- Red light districts
- Heidi Fleiss
- Sexual Slaves

- Tricks/johns
- Pimps
- Gentlemen's clubs
- Pro Doms
- William masters and Virginia Johnson
- "Bawdy House" or "disorderly house"
- Obscenity statutes
- Trafficking
- Gayle Rubin
- COYOTE and PONY
- Margo St. James
- NOW
- HIRE
- WWW
- Lusty Lady

SAMPLE TEST ITEMS: TRUE/FALSE

1. T F The term sex work serves a dual purpose.

2. T F There is little to no gender or class bias in research on sex work and sex workers.

3. T F Beware of researchers who generalize their findings to all prostitutes, all porn workers, etc.

4. T F In the West, prostitution is not intimately related to the history of pornography.

5. T F Some common stereotypes about prostitutes are that like sex with strangers, they are older women, and they have been trained professionally to have sex.

MULTIPLE CHOICE

1. Researcher Priscilla Alexander estimate _____% of prostitutes in America are street based.
   a. 10
   b. 15
   c. 20
   d. 25
   e. 30

2. Heidi Fleiss and Sydney Biddle Barrows are famous:
   a. erotic dancers
   b. international peep show experts
   c. sexologists who study the sex industry
   d. madams
   e. porno actresses

3. Pro Doms are:
   a. prostitutes who only offer their clients oral sex
   b. professionals who offer their clients sadomasochistic scenes
   c. bouncers who work in houses of prostitution
   d. are high class peep show workers who have international acclaim
   e. the only types of sex work that is legal in Japan

4. Surrogate partners' primary responsibility is to:
   a. provide their clients with recreational sex
   b. Teach clients sexual skills and assist in the clients' therapy
   c. Have a women's babies
   d. Train prostitutes in the art of hot sexual techniques
   e. Work in conjunction with university researcher to develop sex techniques

5. Prostitution is illegal in every state in the United States, except in certain counties of:
   a. Alabama
   b. California
   c. Delaware
   d. Nevada
   e. Pennsylvania

DISCUSSION ITEMS

Before reading this chapter, did you believe the sex industry encompassed so many different kinds of sex work? Identify even more forms of sex work that are not mentioned in this chapter?

Discuss the international sex work issues, and brainstorm in terms of how these global issues can be handled more systematically and effectively.

STUDY QUESTIONS

Identify the issues and limitations of the research on sex work.

List the stereotypes about sex workers, and explain how these stereotypes can be challenged and finally "put to rest"?

ANSWERS

True/False:
  1. T
  2. F
  3. T
  4. F
  5. F

Multiple Choice:
  1. A
  2. D
  3. B
  4. B
  5. D

CHAPTER 28

Sex Sells, Especially to Web Surfers: Internet Porn a Booming, Billion-Dollar Industry

Jeordan Legon

SUMMARY

The online porn industry has made getting sexual material more accessible and anonymous than ever before, while generating lots of revenue. However, with the lack of regulation on the Internet, many are concerned about some of the potentially negative effects that such easy access to porn can have on our children, our relationships, and our society.

IDENTIFICATIONS: NAMES/CONCEPTS/TERMS

- Filtering
- Spam
- "Mousetrapping"

SAMPLE TEST ITEMS: TRUE/FALSE

1. T F   According to the article, there are over 1.3 million pornography websites operating on the Internet.

2. T   F   Though the online porn industry generates $1 billion annually, its popularity is predicted to fall and produce much less profit in the future.

3. T   F   Some experts believe that Internet porn is creating unrealistic expectations among couples in their real-life sexual relationships.

MULTIPLE CHOICE

1. "Mousetrapping" is when an online consumer:
   a. cannot exit out of a particular website.
   b. is bombarded by pop-up windows.
   c. is sent to other sites involuntarily when closing out one window.
   d. is charged hidden fees when purchasing online.
   e. has their personal information sold to other online porn companies.

2. David Burt, spokesperson for a Web-filtering company, says that people should be concerned with Internet porn primarily due to:
   a. its potentially destructive effects on users' romantic relationships.
   b. becoming addicted to online porn.
   c. the misogynistic way porn portrays women.
   d. the ease with which children can accidentally stumble onto porn sites.
   e. the huge amount of money that people sometimes unwittingly spend on porn sites.

DISCUSSION ITEM

How do you think Internet porn should be regulated?

STUDY QUESTIONS

What were some of the suggestions that Kathee Brewer, technology editor of the porn industry news site AVN Online, had about having the online porn industry policing itself?

How has online porn helped to pioneer many of the new online technologies?

ANSWERS

True/False:
  1. T
  2. F
  3. T

Multiple Choice:
  1. C
  2. D